Practise
Fractions and Decimals

KS3
Age 11–14
Hilary Koll and Steve Mills

Contents

Introduction

Practise Fractions and Decimals

Practise Fractions and Decimals is for anyone who is struggling to understand concepts in these topics like equivalence, adding and subtracting fractions, converting between fractions and decimals, and all the other difficult ideas usually covered in maths lessons at Key Stage 3. Fractions and decimals are topics that most people find difficult at first, but this simple, step-by-step approach should have you adding and subtracting fractions and ordering decimals in no time.

Part 1 (pages 3–14) of this book is all about understanding fractions and decimals and equivalence. Part 2 (pages 19–30) deals with proportion, improper fractions and mixed numbers, and it provides strategies for adding and subtracting fractions and ordering fractions and decimals. Also covered is using common denominators.

How to use *Practise*

Work through each section in order, reading all the clues and tips in the margins as you go through the exercises. You will need to cut out the cards in the centre of the book to use for some activities. Make sure you keep these cards in a safe place, such as an envelope, so you can re-use them.

When you feel confident with what is written on a particular page, turn over and try to answer the questions on the next page. Carefully mark all your answers and see how you got on. If you still have any difficulties and feel you need some more practice, try some of the activities again or re-read the tips and comments in the margins. If you feel confident and have got most of the questions right, move on to the next section.

You might find it helpful to make a list of all the key words that you come across in this book and write down the meanings. This will help you when you try to answer the questions.

First published in 2007
exclusively for WHSmith by
Hodder Education, part of Hachette Livre UK,
338 Euston Road
London NW1 3BH

Impression number   10 9 8 7 6 5 4 3 2
Year   2010 2009 2008
Text and illustrations © Hodder Murray 2007

Text: Hilary Koll and Steve Mills (e-mail: info@cmeprojects.com)
Cover illustration by Sally Newton Illustrations
Typeset by Fakenham Photosetting Limited, Fakenham, Norfolk
Printed and bound in Spain

A CIP record for this book is available from the British Library

ISBN 978 0 340 94289 5

What are fractions?

Practice

Fractions describe *parts* of whole things.
- Fractions have one number on top of another.
  The number on the *bottom* is called the **denominator**.

  These fractions are related:
  They all have a denominator of 5.

  $\frac{3}{5}$ $\frac{4}{5}$ $\frac{1}{5}$ $\frac{5}{5}$ $\frac{8}{5}$

- Fractions with a denominator of 5 are related because, for each of them, a whole thing has been split into **5 equal parts**.
  The whole thing could be anything such as:

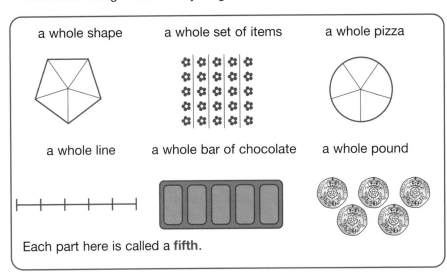

a whole shape   a whole set of items   a whole pizza

a whole line   a whole bar of chocolate   a whole pound

Each part here is called a **fifth**.

- The denominator shows how many equal parts the whole has been split into.
- The number on the *top* of a fraction is called the **numerator**.
  The numerator shows how many of the equal parts there are.

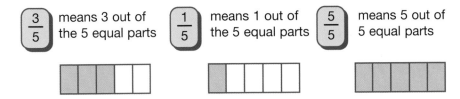

$\frac{3}{5}$ means 3 out of the 5 equal parts $\frac{1}{5}$ means 1 out of the 5 equal parts $\frac{5}{5}$ means 5 out of 5 equal parts

Try it

- Cut out the fraction cards on page 15.
- Practise describing what each fraction means.

Word wise

The denominator is like a family name or surname.

A family name or surname is used to show that people are *related*.

The denominator of a fraction shows us which fractions are *related*.

The numerator is like a first name. It is needed so that people can tell the difference between other people and their families.

To remember which is which, use this phrase:

The denominator is

down under the numerator.

Clues and tips

Here, the top number (the numerator) tells you how many equal parts to shade.

A common mistake

Some people think that the bottom number tells you how many parts are *not* shaded. But they are WRONG.

The bottom number (the denominator) tells you how many equal parts there are *altogether*.

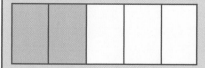

This shows 2 out of 5, or $\frac{2}{5}$ (NOT $\frac{2}{3}$)

Starting with the denominator, count the total number of parts. Put that number on the bottom. Then count the shaded ones. Put that number on the top.

What next?

If you have managed to get these right, go on to page 5. If not, read the tips above again. You might find that the next page also helps you.

Try it yourself!

1. Describe each fraction in words and shade each picture accordingly.

$\frac{2}{3}$ **2 out of 3 equal parts**

$\frac{1}{6}$ _____

$\frac{7}{9}$ _____

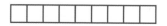

$\frac{4}{5}$ _____

$\frac{3}{4}$ _____

$\frac{6}{6}$ _____

$\frac{5}{8}$ _____

$\frac{4}{7}$ _____

2. What fraction of each of these circles is shaded?

 —   —   —

 —   —   —

Fractions of amounts in your head

Practice

- Any whole thing (including numbers) can be split into fractional parts.
- Use the cut-out fraction cards on page 15.
- Find every fraction that has a **numerator** of 1, like these:

$$\frac{1}{6} \quad \frac{1}{2} \quad \frac{1}{5} \quad \frac{1}{8} \quad \frac{1}{4} \quad \frac{1}{3}$$

These fractions are called **unit fractions**.

- A unit fraction of any number can be found by dividing it by the **denominator** (bottom number), like this:

$$\boxed{\frac{1}{6}} \text{ of } 54 = 54 \div 6 = 9$$

Try these in your head:

$$\boxed{\frac{1}{3}} \text{ of } 15 \qquad \boxed{\frac{1}{5}} \text{ of } 20 \qquad \boxed{\frac{1}{8}} \text{ of } 16 \qquad \boxed{\frac{1}{7}} \text{ of } 14$$

divide 15 by 3   divide 20 by 5

- Once you can find a unit fraction of a number, you can find *any* fraction of a number by multiplying, like this:

$$\boxed{\frac{5}{6}} \text{ of } 54 \quad 54 \div 6 = 9, \qquad 9 \times 5 = 45$$

one-sixth   five-sixths

Try these in your head:

$$\boxed{\frac{2}{3}} \text{ of } 15 \qquad \boxed{\frac{4}{5}} \text{ of } 20 \qquad \boxed{\frac{5}{8}} \text{ of } 16 \qquad \boxed{\frac{4}{7}} \text{ of } 14$$

divide 15 by 3
to find one-third
then multiply by 2

- Remember: **Divide** by the denominator to find the unit fraction then
  multiply by the numerator.

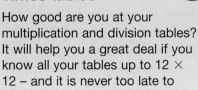

Times tables

How good are you at your multiplication and division tables? It will help you a great deal if you know all your tables up to 12 × 12 – and it is never too late to learn.

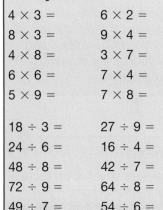

Test yourself

$4 \times 3 =$	$6 \times 2 =$
$8 \times 3 =$	$9 \times 4 =$
$4 \times 8 =$	$3 \times 7 =$
$6 \times 6 =$	$7 \times 4 =$
$5 \times 9 =$	$7 \times 8 =$
$18 \div 3 =$	$27 \div 9 =$
$24 \div 6 =$	$16 \div 4 =$
$48 \div 8 =$	$42 \div 7 =$
$72 \div 9 =$	$64 \div 8 =$
$49 \div 7 =$	$54 \div 6 =$

If you know these, then you probably know most of your tables. If there are some you do not know, LEARN them.

Take one fact a day and keep repeating it in different voices and accents. You will soon memorise them.

Try it yourself!

1. **Find the unit fractions of these numbers in your head.**

   $\frac{1}{5}$ of 15 _____ $\frac{1}{8}$ of 16 _____ $\frac{1}{5}$ of 35 _____

   $\frac{1}{6}$ of 24 _____ $\frac{1}{9}$ of 45 _____ $\frac{1}{7}$ of 21 _____

   $\frac{1}{3}$ of 27 _____ $\frac{1}{7}$ of 42 _____ $\frac{1}{8}$ of 48 _____

   $\frac{1}{4}$ of 28 _____ $\frac{1}{9}$ of 63 _____ $\frac{1}{8}$ of 64 _____

   $\frac{1}{3}$ of 33 _____ $\frac{1}{6}$ of 36 _____ $\frac{1}{7}$ of 49 _____

2. **Find the fractions of these amounts in your head.**

   $\frac{2}{5}$ of £15 _____ $\frac{3}{8}$ of 16 m _____ $\frac{4}{5}$ of 35 kg _____

   $\frac{5}{6}$ of £24 _____ $\frac{4}{9}$ of 45 m _____ $\frac{3}{7}$ of 21 kg _____

   $\frac{2}{3}$ of £27 _____ $\frac{2}{7}$ of 42 m _____ $\frac{5}{8}$ of 48 kg _____

   $\frac{3}{4}$ of £28 _____ $\frac{8}{9}$ of 63 m _____ $\frac{3}{8}$ of 64 kg _____

   $\frac{2}{3}$ of £33 _____ $\frac{5}{6}$ of 36 m _____ $\frac{6}{7}$ of 49 kg _____

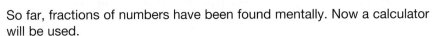

Fractions of amounts with a calculator

Practice

So far, fractions of numbers have been found mentally. Now a calculator will be used.

- When working out a fraction of an amount in our heads, the amount is **divided** by the **denominator** and **multiplied** by the **numerator**.

$\dfrac{5}{6}$ of £24

To answer this using a calculator, key in **24 ÷ 6 × 5** to get the answer 20.

- So it can be worked out with a calculator *exactly as it is in our heads*.
- Sometimes, however, teachers show a different way to find fractions of amounts on a calculator. It is actually the same method, but in a different order. Look at this:

When three numbers are multiplied or divided together, it can be done in any order and the answer will be the same.

24 ÷ 6 × 5 gives the same answer as **5 ÷ 6 × 24**

Try it on a calculator.
- Teachers sometimes show this second way because it is in the order that the numbers appear in the question.

$\dfrac{5}{6}$ of £24   **5 ÷ 6 × 24**

Notice that the amount is still divided by the denominator.
- Learn to look at a fraction and think of it as a **division question**.

Try it

Pick a fraction card and write it as a division question.

$\boxed{\dfrac{4}{5}}$ = 4 ÷ 5

- So, to find a fraction of an amount on a calculator, just key in the fraction as a division question and then multiply by the amount.

$\dfrac{4}{5}$ of £30 = 4 ÷ 5 × 30

Two ways

This page shows two different ways of finding a fraction of an amount on a calculator.

It does not matter which way is chosen.

Whether it is done the same way as the mental method, or by thinking of the fraction as a division question and multiplying, the answer will be the same.

Word wise

The word 'of' in maths is usually shown by the multiplication sign.

$\dfrac{5}{6}$ of 24   is $\dfrac{5}{6}$ × 24

Remember to work from top to bottom: numerator divided by denominator.

Clues and tips

Remember to work from top to bottom: numerator divided by denominator.

Two ways

It does not matter which method you choose to answer question 2 (see page 7).

Decimal difficulties

Watch out for any answers which appear on the calculator that do not make sense. For example, how much is £24.4444444?

If you are talking about money, then round the answer to the nearest pence – £24.44.

What next?

If you are fine with this topic, go on to page 9.

If you find the second method on page 7 difficult, use the mental method on page 5.

Try it yourself!

1. **Write these fractions as division questions.**

   $\dfrac{2}{5}$ _____ $\dfrac{3}{8}$ _____ $\dfrac{4}{5}$ _____

   $\dfrac{5}{6}$ _____ $\dfrac{4}{9}$ _____ $\dfrac{3}{7}$ _____

2. **Find the fractions of these amounts on a calculator.**

   $\dfrac{2}{5}$ of £75 _____ $\dfrac{3}{8}$ of 128 m _____ $\dfrac{4}{5}$ of 105 kg _____

   $\dfrac{5}{6}$ of £72 _____ $\dfrac{4}{9}$ of 135 m _____ $\dfrac{3}{7}$ of 91 kg _____

   $\dfrac{2}{3}$ of £69 _____ $\dfrac{2}{7}$ of 182 m _____ $\dfrac{5}{8}$ of 192 kg _____

3. **Find the fractions of these amounts on a calculator. Note that these answers may not be whole numbers.**

   $\dfrac{2}{5}$ of £53 _____ $\dfrac{3}{8}$ of 60 m _____ $\dfrac{4}{5}$ of 49 kg _____

   $\dfrac{5}{6}$ of £27 _____ $\dfrac{4}{9}$ of 55 m _____ $\dfrac{3}{7}$ of 72 kg _____

   $\dfrac{2}{3}$ of £81 _____ $\dfrac{2}{7}$ of 34 m _____ $\dfrac{5}{8}$ of 102 kg _____

   $\dfrac{3}{4}$ of £73 _____ $\dfrac{8}{9}$ of 75 m _____ $\dfrac{3}{8}$ of 95 kg _____

Equivalence and simplest form

Practice

- Look at these two shapes. If both shapes were bars of chocolate, and you were given

$$\frac{4}{5} \text{ or } \frac{8}{10}$$

$$\frac{4}{5}$$

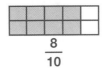

$$\frac{8}{10}$$

which would give you more chocolate? Neither. These fractions are **equivalent**.

- Equivalent fractions have the same value but are made using different digits.

$$\frac{4}{5} = \frac{8}{10}$$

All of the fractions below are equivalent to one half.

$$\frac{5}{10}$$

$$\frac{3}{6}$$

$$\frac{2}{4}$$

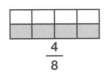

$$\frac{4}{8}$$

- To find fractions that are equivalent, the top *and* bottom numbers can be multiplied or divided by the same number.

$$\div 5 \quad \frac{5}{10} \quad \frac{1}{2} \quad \div 5$$

$$\times 3 \quad \frac{1}{2} \quad \frac{3}{6} \quad \times 3$$

$$\div 2 \quad \frac{2}{4} \quad \frac{1}{2} \quad \div 2$$

$$\times 4 \quad \frac{1}{2} \quad \frac{4}{8} \quad \times 4$$

These fractions are all equivalent to one half.

> As long as the top and bottom numbers are multiplied or divided by the same number, the new fraction will be equivalent.

Try it

Pick a fraction card and give at least three other equivalent fractions.

$$\boxed{\frac{4}{5}} \quad \frac{8}{10} \quad \frac{40}{50} \quad \frac{24}{30}$$

- To change a fraction to its **simplest form**, divide until there is no other number (except 1) that divides exactly into the top *and* bottom numbers.

$$\div 2 \quad \div 4 \quad \div 2$$
$$\frac{128}{240} = \frac{64}{120} = \frac{16}{30} = \frac{8}{15}$$
$$\div 2 \quad \div 4 \quad \div 2$$

$\frac{128}{240}$ in its simplest form is $\frac{8}{15}$

because there is no other number (except for 1) that divides into 8 and 15

Simplest form

When changing a fraction to its simplest form, always look to see what number will divide exactly into the numerator and into the denominator.

$$\div 5 \quad \frac{45}{100} \quad \frac{9}{20} \quad \div 5$$

After dividing, check that there is not another whole number that will divide into both numbers. If there is not, the fraction is in its simplest form.

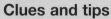

Clues and tips

An equivalent fraction can be made by multiplying or dividing the numerator *and* the denominator by the same number.

Simplest form

To change a fraction to its simplest form, *divide* the numerator and denominator by the same number. Keep doing this until there are no other numbers (except 1) that will divide into both numbers.

What next?

Make up more equivalent fractions using the fraction cards cut from page 15.

Practise your tables if you find it difficult to multiply and divide numbers in your head (see page 5).

Try it yourself!

1. **Write an equivalent fraction by multiplying or dividing as shown.**

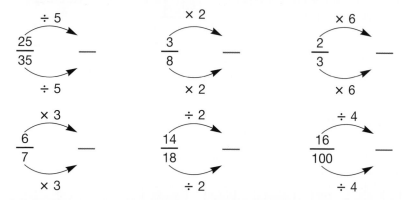

2. **Check to see which fractions are equivalent to $\frac{1}{4}$.**

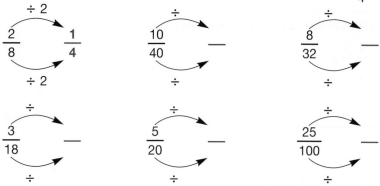

3. **Change these fractions to their simplest form.**

$\frac{24}{30}$ _____

$\frac{80}{100}$ _____

$\frac{36}{48}$ _____

$\frac{16}{68}$ _____

Denominators of 10, 100, etc. – decimals

Practice

Now you are going to learn how to convert fractions to **decimals**.

Decimals are like fractions. They are used to describe parts of whole things.

> The first step is to change the fraction to an **equivalent** one that has a **denominator** (bottom number) of 10 or 100, like these:
>
>
>
> Notice that each new fraction has a denominator of 10 or 100. Remember the new fraction is equivalent – it is worth the same.

- For a decimal, the columns after the decimal point stand for **tenths** and **hundredths**.

H T U . t h
3 2 0 . 2 7

So   0.2 means two-tenths $\frac{2}{10}$

and   0.09 means nine-hundredths $\frac{9}{100}$

and   0.37 means thirty-seven-hundredths $\frac{37}{100}$

- So, to convert a *fraction to a decimal,* it is first changed to an equivalent fraction with the denominator of 10 or 100.

  Then the digits of the **numerator** are written in the correct columns to make the decimal.

  So, three-fifths or six-tenths are both the decimal **0.6**

  So, seven-twentieths or thirty-five-hundredths are both the decimal 0.35

Try it

Do this for each of the fraction cards cut from page 15.

Try it yourself!

1. Write each of these fractions as a decimal.

$\frac{4}{10}$ ___0.4___ $\frac{1}{10}$ _____ $\frac{6}{10}$ _____

$\frac{8}{100}$ ___0.08___ $\frac{2}{100}$ _____ $\frac{9}{100}$ _____

$\frac{99}{100}$ ___0.99___ $\frac{36}{100}$ _____ $\frac{61}{100}$ _____

2. Convert each fraction into an equivalent one with a denominator of 10 or 100. Then write the fractions as decimals.

$\frac{3}{5} = \frac{6}{10} =$ ___0.6___ $\frac{1}{2} = \frac{\ }{10} =$ _____

$\frac{1}{50} = \frac{\ }{100} =$ _____ $\frac{3}{20} = \frac{\ }{100} =$ _____

$\frac{21}{50} = \frac{\ }{100} =$ _____ $\frac{18}{20} = \frac{\ }{100} =$ _____

3. Write these as fractions then change to their simplest form.

0.4 ___$\frac{4}{10}$ or $\frac{2}{5}$___   0.6 _____   0.8 _____

0.02 _____   0.05 _____   0.08 _____

0.25 _____   0.75 _____   0.22 _____

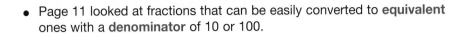
Converting to decimals with a calculator

Practice

- Page 11 looked at fractions that can be easily converted to **equivalent** ones with a **denominator** of 10 or 100.

- However, NOT ALL fractions can be changed in this way.

This fraction *cannot* be changed to an equivalent one with a denominator of 10 or 100.

- This fraction *can* be written as a **decimal**, but a calculator has to be used to find out what it is.
- Remember that a fraction can be thought of as a **division question**. So, just key the division question into a calculator and it will display the fraction as a decimal.

$$\frac{5}{17} = 5 \div 17 = \boxed{0.294117647}$$

The answer is then rounded so that it has 2 digits after the decimal point. It is said that the answer has been rounded to 2 **decimal places**.

So $\frac{5}{17}$ is the decimal 0.29 (to 2 decimal places).

- Some calculators have a key marked $\boxed{a\%}$

This can help you to change between fractions and decimals.

Key in $\frac{5}{9}$ as $\boxed{5}$ $\boxed{a\%}$ $\boxed{9}$ $\boxed{=}$ then keep pressing $\boxed{a\%}$ to change between fractions and decimals.

Or key in a decimal followed by $\boxed{=}$ and then $\boxed{a\%}$ to get the fraction in its **simplest form**.

Recurring decimals

Sometimes a decimal has a digit or digits that repeat, like 0.3333333333 or 0.272727272727.

These decimals are called recurring decimals.

Rounding

When a fraction cannot be expressed as an equivalent one with a denominator of 10 or 100 (or 1000 and so on), the decimal will probably have many digits after the decimal point.

Rather than writing all the digits, the number is rounded to 1 or 2 decimal places (so that the answer has 1 or 2 digits after the decimal point).

The words 'decimal places' can be shortened to dp.

Try it

Cut out the fraction cards on page 17.

Use a calculator to express each fraction as a decimal to 2 decimal places.

  5 ÷ 9 =
0.56 (to 2 dp)

Try it yourself!

1. **Convert these fractions to decimals with a calculator. Write the answer shown on your calculator display.**

$\frac{1}{3}$ _____ $\frac{2}{3}$ _____

$\frac{4}{11}$ _____ $\frac{5}{13}$ _____

$\frac{4}{9}$ _____ $\frac{3}{7}$ _____

$\frac{2}{11}$ _____ $\frac{3}{13}$ _____

$\frac{4}{17}$ _____ $\frac{5}{15}$ _____

$\frac{4}{7}$ _____ $\frac{7}{9}$ _____

2. **Convert these fractions to decimals with a calculator. Round the answers to 2 decimal places.**

$\frac{3}{11}$ _____ $\frac{1}{9}$ _____

$\frac{1}{6}$ _____ $\frac{24}{29}$ _____

$\frac{7}{11}$ _____ $\frac{11}{13}$ _____

$\frac{21}{37}$ _____ $\frac{5}{9}$ _____

$\frac{12}{23}$ _____ $\frac{27}{29}$ _____

$\frac{15}{17}$ _____ $\frac{41}{99}$ _____

$\frac{12}{29}$ _____ $\frac{6}{17}$ _____

$\frac{9}{11}$ _____

Activity cards

First set of fraction cards

$\dfrac{1}{2}$	$\dfrac{3}{4}$	$\dfrac{7}{10}$	$\dfrac{1}{25}$
$\dfrac{1}{5}$	$\dfrac{2}{5}$	$\dfrac{9}{10}$	$\dfrac{4}{25}$
$\dfrac{1}{4}$	$\dfrac{3}{10}$	$\dfrac{3}{20}$	$\dfrac{1}{50}$
$\dfrac{1}{10}$	$\dfrac{3}{5}$	$\dfrac{11}{20}$	$\dfrac{13}{50}$
$\dfrac{1}{20}$	$\dfrac{4}{5}$	$\dfrac{19}{20}$	$\dfrac{49}{50}$

Activity cards

Activity cards

$\dfrac{2}{9}$	$\dfrac{8}{9}$	$\dfrac{2}{7}$	$\dfrac{5}{17}$
$\dfrac{11}{17}$	$\dfrac{1}{3}$	$\dfrac{6}{7}$	$\dfrac{4}{9}$
$\dfrac{23}{24}$	$\dfrac{1}{6}$	$\dfrac{3}{13}$	$\dfrac{1}{9}$
$\dfrac{17}{19}$	$\dfrac{2}{3}$	$\dfrac{5}{19}$	$\dfrac{3}{11}$
$\dfrac{4}{99}$	$\dfrac{5}{6}$	$\dfrac{4}{7}$	$\dfrac{5}{11}$

Activity cards

Proportion

- Now that you understand what fractions and decimals are, you can begin to solve **proportion** problems. The word 'proportion' means 'part of the whole', like this:

> A class has 24 girls and 8 boys. What proportion of the class is girls? (i.e. What part of the whole class is girls?) ← This can be answered using a fraction, a decimal or a percentage.

There are 32 pupils in the class and 24 are girls,

so $\frac{24}{32}$ is the answer as a fraction.

This fraction can be given in its **simplest form**

Three-quarters as a decimal is **0.75**.
Three-quarters as a percentage is **75%**.

Any of the answers $\frac{3}{4}$, 0.75 or 75% is acceptable.

- Try this one:

> A class has 16 girls and 14 boys. What proportion of the class is girls?

There are 30 pupils in the class and 16 are girls,

so $\frac{16}{30}$ is the answer as a fraction.

This fraction can be given in its simplest form

Use a calculator to find this as a decimal.
8 ÷ 15 = 0.5333333333 or **0.53** to 2 dp.
As a percentage, 0.53 is **53%**.

- If you are given a proportion and asked to find 'how many . . .' you will need to **multiply** the proportion by the whole.

- Try this one:

> The proportion of girls in a class is $\frac{3}{4}$, 0.75 or 75%. There are 32 pupils in the class. How many are girls?

$\frac{3}{4} \times 32$ or **0.75 × 32**   or **75% × 32**

Key any of these into the calculator to get the answer **24**.

- Remember:
A fraction can be written as a division question: $\frac{3}{4}$ is **3 ÷ 4**

The % sign means 'out of 100' or 'divided by 100': **75%** is **75 ÷ 100**

Clues and tips

At the bottom of page 13, the calculator key was introduced. This key helps to convert between fractions and decimals. It also helps to change a fraction to its simplest form.

Key in the fraction $\frac{16}{36}$ like this:

and when the equals button is pressed, the display shows the fraction $\frac{4}{9}$ like this:

This is $\frac{16}{36}$ in its simplest form.

What next?

Once you get a feel for fractions and decimals, solving problems becomes easier. However, if you are still finding these difficult, you might want to look back at pages 9 and 13.

If you struggle with percentages, you might find the *Practise Percentages* book in this series useful.

If you find this sort of question okay, move on to page 21 to look at other types of fractions.

Try it yourself!

1. **What proportion of each of these classes is girls? Give each answer as a fraction in its simplest form.**

A class has 16 girls and 20 boys:

$$\frac{16}{36} \quad \xrightarrow{\div 4} \quad \frac{4}{9}$$

$\div 4$

A class has:

8 girls and 24 boys   12 girls and 20 boys

15 girls and 25 boys   12 girls and 24 boys

2. **Solve these proportion problems, giving each answer as a fraction in its simplest form and as a decimal (to 2 decimal places).**

In a box of chocolates 35 were milk, 18 were plain and 7 were white chocolate. What proportion of the chocolates was milk chocolate?

_____

In a box of chocolates 29 were milk, 27 were plain and 7 were white chocolate. What proportion of the chocolates was plain chocolate?

_____

3. **Solve these questions.**

The proportion of girls in a class is $\frac{5}{7}$. There are 35 pupils in the class. How many are girls?

_____

The proportion of girls in a class is $\frac{3}{8}$. There are 32 pupils in the class. How many are girls?

_____

Mixed numbers and improper fractions

Practice

- Fractions are used to describe parts of a whole. But what happens when you want to describe some parts that make up *more than one whole*? Here, 5 quarters are shaded:

This can be written in two ways:

five-quarters $\frac{5}{4}$ or one whole and one quarter $1\frac{1}{4}$

The first way involves writing an **improper fraction**.

With an improper fraction, the number on top (the **numerator**) is *larger* than the number on the bottom (the **denominator**).

The second way involves writing a **mixed number**.
A mixed number has a whole number *and* a fraction.

- It is important to be able to change from one form to the other.

Converting *from* improper fractions *to* mixed numbers

- Ask yourself:
  How many lots of the denominator are in the numerator? $\frac{13}{5}$
  How many 5s in 13?

- Work out the answer and write it with a remainder ... **2 r 3**
  The first number is the whole number.

  The remainder is the numerator of the fraction.
  The denominator stays the same.

Converting *from* mixed numbers *to* improper fractions

- First do this multiplication:
  whole number × denominator $2\frac{3}{5}$ $2 \times 5 = 10$

  (This gives you how many fifths there are in the 2 whole ones.)

- Then add on the numerator (the extra fifths) ... $10 + 3 = 13$
  This is the new numerator of the improper fraction. $\frac{13}{5}$
  The denominator stays the same.

Try it

Write improper fractions to change to mixed numbers and vice versa.

Remember this

It is easy to recognise decimals that are *more than one whole*. The digits to the left of the decimal point tell you how many wholes you have, whilst the digits to the right of the decimal point tell you about the parts.

0.51 means no whole ones and 51 hundredths

34.5 means 34 whole ones and 5 tenths

Watch out

Remember that the numerator must be larger than the denominator in an improper fraction.

Choose any whole number and any fraction to make a mixed number.

Try it yourself!

1. **Convert these improper fractions to mixed numbers.**

$\frac{8}{3}$ _____ $\frac{14}{3}$ _____

$\frac{7}{5}$ _____ $\frac{19}{8}$ _____

$\frac{21}{9}$ _____ $\frac{9}{7}$ _____

$\frac{23}{4}$ _____ $\frac{14}{5}$ _____

$\frac{25}{6}$ _____ $\frac{9}{2}$ _____

$\frac{37}{7}$ _____ $\frac{34}{5}$ _____

$\frac{42}{5}$ _____ $\frac{50}{8}$ _____

$\frac{79}{9}$ _____

2. **Convert these mixed numbers to improper fractions.**

$3\frac{1}{4}$ _____ $5\frac{3}{4}$ _____

$4\frac{1}{5}$ _____ $4\frac{2}{3}$ _____

$2\frac{5}{8}$ _____ $3\frac{1}{6}$ _____

$6\frac{1}{2}$ _____ $8\frac{1}{3}$ _____

$5\frac{5}{6}$ _____ $7\frac{3}{4}$ _____

$6\frac{4}{5}$ _____ $2\frac{3}{8}$ _____

$4\frac{1}{7}$ _____ $3\frac{5}{9}$ _____

$5\frac{6}{7}$ _____

Adding and subtracting fractions

Practice

To add or subtract fractions, first make sure that the denominators of the fractions are the same. Then it is easy. Look at this:

$$\frac{3}{5} + \frac{1}{5} = \frac{4}{5}$$

Notice that the fractions being added have the same **denominators**.

The **numerators** are added. The denominator stays the same.

Try it

Find two fraction cards with the same denominator.
Add them together.

$$\frac{4}{10} + \frac{9}{10} = \frac{13}{10} = 1\frac{3}{10}$$

If your answer is an improper fraction, change it to a mixed number.
Do this several times to get the hang of it.

Subtraction is the same. Just subtract the numerators.

- What do you do if the denominators are *not* the same?

$$\frac{2}{5} + \frac{3}{4} = ?$$

- Do you remember how to change a fraction to an **equivalent** one? Remind yourself how by looking back at page 9. Change each fraction to an equivalent one so that they both have the *same* denominator.

To do this, look at both denominators. $\frac{2}{5}$ $\frac{3}{4}$

Q: What is the lowest number that both 4 and 5 divide exactly into?
A: 20

So, change both fractions to equivalent ones each with a denominator of 20:

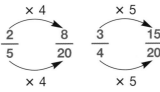

So, now the question is:

$$\frac{8}{20} + \frac{15}{20} = \frac{23}{20} = 1\frac{3}{20}$$

Remind yourself how by looking back at page 9.

A common mistake

The most common mistake when adding fractions is to add the denominators too. The answer to

$$\frac{1}{4} + \frac{1}{4} =$$

. . . is not $\frac{2}{8}$

. . . it is $\frac{2}{4}$

Denominator choosing

Sometimes it is not necessary to change both fractions to equivalent ones. Look at this question:

$$\frac{5}{6} + \frac{8}{12} =$$

Q: What is the lowest number that both 6 and 12 divide exactly into?
A: 12

Both fractions need to have the denominator 12, but one of them already has. Only the first fraction needs to change.

Clues and tips

If the denominators are the same, all you have to do is add the numerators (for addition) or subtract the numerators (for subtraction).

The denominator always stays the same.

Watch out

In question 2, there is quite a lot to think about when adding or subtracting fractions with different denominators. Start by deciding on the lowest number into which both denominators go. This will be the new denominator.

What next?

This section is quite difficult and you may be struggling with choosing an appropriate denominator, or with changing fractions to equivalent ones. Look back over page 9 to revise this. Knowing your tables will also help you with this (see page 5).

Try it yourself!

1. **Add or subtract these fractions. Notice that the denominators of each pair of fractions are the *same*. If your answer is an improper fraction, change it to a mixed number.**

$\dfrac{1}{5} + \dfrac{3}{5}$ _____ $\dfrac{2}{9} + \dfrac{4}{9}$ _____ $\dfrac{6}{7} + \dfrac{4}{7}$ _____

$\dfrac{6}{10} + \dfrac{7}{10}$ _____ $\dfrac{3}{8} + \dfrac{5}{8}$ _____ $\dfrac{3}{4} + \dfrac{3}{4}$ _____

$\dfrac{7}{11} - \dfrac{5}{11}$ _____ $\dfrac{5}{6} - \dfrac{1}{6}$ _____ $\dfrac{4}{5} - \dfrac{3}{5}$ _____

$\dfrac{11}{12} - \dfrac{3}{12}$ _____ $\dfrac{8}{9} - \dfrac{3}{9}$ _____ $\dfrac{9}{13} - \dfrac{5}{13}$ _____

2. **Add or subtract these fractions. Notice that the denominators of each pair of fractions are *NOT* the same.**

   You will need to change one or both of the fractions to equivalent ones so that the denominators of both fractions *are* the same.

$\dfrac{1}{5} + \dfrac{4}{10}$ _____ $\dfrac{6}{12} + \dfrac{4}{6}$ _____

$\dfrac{3}{5} + \dfrac{1}{2}$ _____ $\dfrac{3}{4} + \dfrac{3}{5}$ _____

$\dfrac{3}{4} - \dfrac{2}{3}$ _____ $\dfrac{2}{3} - \dfrac{1}{5}$ _____

$\dfrac{6}{7} - \dfrac{3}{14}$ _____ $\dfrac{5}{6} - \dfrac{2}{5}$ _____

Ordering decimals

Practice

- Make sure that you know what each digit in a decimal stands for.

A **tenth 0.1** is the same as

$\frac{1}{10}$

and a **hundredth 0.01** is

$\frac{1}{100}$

tenths   hundredths   thousandths

TU . t h th
93.684

whole ones . parts

Because tenths are larger than hundredths, it is easy to see that:

 0.4 is larger than **0.04**

- However, most people find this next bit difficult:
With **whole numbers**, the more digits a number has, the larger it is.

This is *not* necessarily true for decimals.

Look at this:

0.4 is larger than **0.38**

- Because tenths are larger than hundredths, the tenths must be compared first. **0.4** has **4 tenths** and **0.38** only has **3 tenths** and some **hundredths**.
- When ordering decimals, begin by comparing the digit on the left and, if they are the same, move to the right to compare the next digit, etc.

| 0.6821 | 0.776 | 0.69 | 0.8 | 0.681 |

Which number has most tenths? ⟶ 0.8

Which has the next greatest number of tenths? ⟶ 0.776

Which numbers have the next greatest number of tenths?
   0.6821   0.69   0.681

Which of these has most hundredths? ⟶ 0.69

Which numbers have the next greatest number of hundredths?
   0.6821   0.681

Which of these has most thousandths? ⟶ 0.6821

Which is the smallest number? ⟶ 0.681

So, the order, from largest to smallest, is:

   0.8   0.776   0.69   0.6821   0.681

Know your decimals

Remind yourself about decimals by looking again at pages 11 and 12.

0.8 is larger than 0.75

Decimal difficulties

It is sometimes easier to see this if 0.4 is thought of as 0.40.

If zeros are put on the end of the numbers with the fewest digits so they have the *same* number of digits, it is sometimes much easier to order them, like this:

0.8000
0.7760
0.6900
0.6821
0.6810

Put on extra zeros

Write zeros at the end of the decimal with the fewer digits so that both decimals have the same number of digits. This may help to decide which is larger.

Comparing fractions

For question 2, it might help to write out all the fractions on to small pieces of paper and to move them around to order them. Remember to start by comparing the tenths, and if the number of tenths is the same, compare the hundredths and so on.

What next?

You will need to be able to order decimals for the ideas on the next few pages. If you have been finding this difficult, make sure you write the zeros on the ends of the numbers so that all decimals have the same number of digits. This should help you with ordering. Otherwise, go on to page 27.

Try it yourself!

1. **Tick the larger decimal in each pair.**

0.40 ✓	0.38	0.8	0.753
0.82	0.81	0.45	0.54
0.82	0.823	0.6	0.603
0.9	0.88	0.751	0.7
0.151	0.21	0.31	0.3
0.3	0.295	0.863	0.86
0.274	0.2741	0.73	0.743

2. **Put each set of decimals in order of size from largest to smallest.**

0.134   0.413   0.314   0.14   0.3

largest _____ smallest

0.289   0.892   0.29   0.8   0.28

largest _____ smallest

0.525   0.252   0.52   0.25   0.5

largest _____ smallest

Ordering fractions

Practice

- Ordering fractions can be done in different ways. The first way is about just having a feel for what sizes fractions are.
This fraction wall shows the relative sizes of different simple fractions.

Use the fraction wall to compare and order this set of fractions.

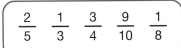

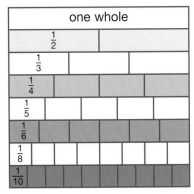

Write the fractions in order from smallest to largest.

smallest [   ] largest

- Sometimes there are too many fractions or the fractions are more difficult to order this way. So, another way is to use a calculator.
First, key in each fraction as a **division question** to change each fraction to a decimal and then *order the decimals*.
Remind yourself how to order decimals by looking again at page 25.

- Order these fractions by ordering the decimals from smallest to largest.

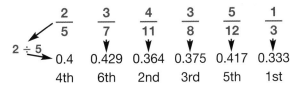

smallest [$\frac{1}{3}$ $\frac{4}{11}$ $\frac{3}{8}$ $\frac{2}{5}$ $\frac{5}{12}$ $\frac{3}{7}$] largest

Try it

Choose any five fraction cards. Convert them to decimals on a calculator and order them.

Do this several times to get the hang of it.

Fraction wall

Each strip of this fraction wall is worth one whole. The second strip shows two halves, the third strip shows three thirds, and so on.

To find the size of a fraction like three-fifths, look at the strip showing 5 equal parts. Count three across from the left to show the size of the fraction $\frac{3}{5}$

Fractions and calculators

Remember that a fraction can be keyed into a calculator as a division question.

Alternatively, some calculators have a (a%) key for converting between fractions and decimals (see page 13).

Fraction wall

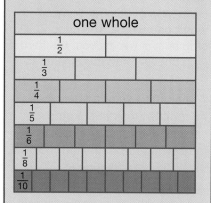

one whole
$\frac{1}{2}$
$\frac{1}{3}$
$\frac{1}{4}$
$\frac{1}{5}$
$\frac{1}{6}$
$\frac{1}{8}$
$\frac{1}{10}$

What next?

Most people find using the fraction wall quite easy, but this is only useful if you have a fraction wall and are ordering simple fractions.

If you were still stuck at the end of page 26, you might be finding this second method difficult. Do not worry, the next page shows a third method for ordering fractions. Have a go and see if you prefer it.

It does not matter which method you use to order fractions.

Try it yourself!

1. Use the fraction wall to compare and order each set of fractions. Write the fractions in order from smallest to largest.

$\frac{4}{5}$ $\frac{3}{4}$ $\frac{5}{6}$ $\frac{1}{8}$ $\frac{7}{8}$ $\frac{3}{5}$ $\frac{5}{10}$ $\frac{2}{3}$ $\frac{5}{8}$ $\frac{5}{6}$

_____   _____

$\frac{2}{3}$ $\frac{1}{4}$ $\frac{2}{5}$ $\frac{1}{8}$ $\frac{3}{10}$ $\frac{7}{10}$ $\frac{3}{4}$ $\frac{4}{6}$ $\frac{5}{8}$ $\frac{1}{2}$

_____   _____

2. Using a calculator, convert each fraction to a decimal. Round any answers to 3 decimal places. Then order the fractions by ordering the decimals.

$\frac{4}{5}$ $\frac{11}{14}$ $\frac{9}{10}$ $\frac{11}{13}$ $\frac{10}{12}$ $\frac{5}{7}$
↓   ↓   ↓   ↓   ↓   ↓
0.8 _____

smallest _____ largest

$\frac{2}{9}$ $\frac{3}{7}$ $\frac{4}{11}$ $\frac{1}{12}$ $\frac{6}{17}$ $\frac{2}{6}$
↓   ↓   ↓   ↓   ↓   ↓
_____

smallest _____ largest

Common denominators

Practice

- Do you remember that when adding and subtracting fractions, you had to change each fraction to an **equivalent** one so that both fractions had the *same* denominator? Look again at page 23.

  The *third way* of ordering fractions is to change all the fractions so that they have the *same* denominator. To do this, look at all the denominators and find the lowest number into which they will all divide.

$$\frac{4}{5} \quad \frac{5}{6} \quad \frac{7}{10} \quad \frac{11}{15} \quad \frac{2}{3}$$

They will all divide into the number 30.

Change all the fractions so that they have the denominator 30.
The new denominator that is chosen for all of the fractions is known as the **common denominator**.
Then the fractions are ordered from smallest to largest by looking at the **numerators**.

$$\frac{24}{30} \quad \frac{25}{30} \quad \frac{21}{30} \quad \frac{22}{30} \quad \frac{20}{30}$$

4th   5th   2nd   3rd   1st

Copy out the original fractions in that order for the answer.

smallest $\frac{2}{3} \quad \frac{7}{10} \quad \frac{11}{15} \quad \frac{4}{5} \quad \frac{5}{6}$ largest

Word wise

A common denominator is a denominator that two fractions share, such as $\frac{3}{5}$ and $\frac{4}{5}$. They share a common denominator of 5.

Here, a denominator is chosen that all the fractions can have in common.

Equivalent fractions

Remember how to change a fraction to an equivalent one?

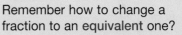
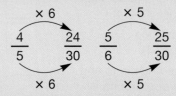

See page 9 to remind yourself how.

Try it

Choose three fraction cards. Look at the denominators. Find the lowest number into which they will all divide.

Convert the fractions to equivalent ones with this as the common denominator.

$$\boxed{\frac{4}{5}} \quad \boxed{\frac{2}{3}} \quad \boxed{\frac{5}{8}}$$

Now order them from smallest to largest by looking at the numerators.
Do this several times to get the hang of it.

Remember this

One way of finding a common denominator is to multiply all the numbers together, e.g.
$5 \times 3 \times 8 = 120$.

Common denominators

More confident with fractions and decimals?

Tick the following topics you feel confident with:

Understanding fractions (pages 3–4) ☐

Finding fractions of amounts in your head (pages 5–6) ☐

Finding fractions of amounts on a calculator (pages 7–8) ☐

Equivalence and simplest form (pages 9–10) ☐

Understanding decimals (pages 11–12) ☐

Converting from fractions to decimals (pages 13–14) ☐

Proportion (pages 19–20) ☐

Mixed numbers and improper fractions (pages 21–22) ☐

Adding and subtracting fractions (pages 23–24) ☐

Ordering decimals (pages 25–26) ☐

Ordering fractions (pages 27–30) ☐

Read through any pages again to make sure you understand.

Why not look at other books in this series to help you with areas you still might be unsure of?

Try it yourself!

1. Convert each of these fractions to **equivalent** ones so that they all have the **common denominator** shown.

   $\dfrac{7}{9}$ $\dfrac{3}{4}$ $\dfrac{5}{6}$ $\dfrac{11}{12}$ $\dfrac{2}{3}$

   $\dfrac{}{36}$ $\dfrac{}{36}$ $\dfrac{}{36}$ $\dfrac{}{36}$ $\dfrac{}{36}$

2. Convert each of these fractions to **equivalent** ones with a **common denominator**. Use this information to list the fractions in order of size from smallest to largest.

   $\dfrac{3}{5}$ $\dfrac{13}{20}$ $\dfrac{5}{8}$

   smallest _____ largest

   $\dfrac{3}{8}$ $\dfrac{2}{3}$ $\dfrac{1}{12}$ $\dfrac{2}{6}$

   smallest _____ largest

   $\dfrac{4}{5}$ $\dfrac{7}{9}$ $\dfrac{13}{15}$ $\dfrac{2}{3}$

   smallest _____ largest

Answers

WHAT ARE FRACTIONS? (PAGE 4)

1. 2 out of 3 equal parts   1 out of 6 equal parts
7 out of 9 equal parts   4 out of 5 equal parts
3 out of 4 equal parts   6 out of 6 equal parts
5 out of 8 equal parts   4 out of 7 equal parts

2. $\dfrac{1}{8}$ $\dfrac{2}{3}$ $\dfrac{1}{6}$ $\dfrac{4}{10}$ $\dfrac{5}{12}$ $\dfrac{7}{10}$

FRACTIONS OF AMOUNTS IN YOUR HEAD (PAGE 6)

1. 3   2   7   4   5   3   9   6   6   7   7   8   11   6   7
2. £6   6 m   28 kg   £20   20 m   9 kg   £18   12 m   30 kg   £21   56 m   24 kg   £22   30 m   42 kg

FRACTIONS OF AMOUNTS WITH A CALCULATOR (PAGE 8)

1. $2 \div 5$ $3 \div 8$ $4 \div 5$ $5 \div 6$ $4 \div 9$ $3 \div 7$
2. £30   48 m   84 kg   £60   60 m   39 kg   £46   52 m   120 kg
3. £21.20   22.5 m   39.2 kg   £22.50   24.44 m   30.86 kg   £54   9.71 m   63.75 kg   £54.75
66.67 m   35.63 kg

EQUIVALENCE AND SIMPLEST FORM (PAGE 10)

1. $\dfrac{5}{7}$ $\dfrac{6}{16}$ $\dfrac{12}{18}$ $\dfrac{18}{21}$ $\dfrac{7}{9}$ $\dfrac{4}{25}$

2. $\dfrac{1}{4}$ $\dfrac{1}{4}$ $\dfrac{1}{4}$ $\dfrac{1}{6}$ $\dfrac{1}{4}$ $\dfrac{1}{4}$

3. $\dfrac{4}{5}$ $\dfrac{4}{5}$ $\dfrac{3}{4}$ $\dfrac{4}{17}$

DENOMINATORS OF 10, 100, ETC. – DECIMALS (PAGE 12)

1. 0.4   0.1   0.6   0.08   0.02   0.09   0.99   0.36   0.61

2. $\dfrac{6}{10} = 0.6$ $\dfrac{5}{10} = 0.5$ $\dfrac{2}{100} = 0.02$ $\dfrac{15}{100} = 0.15$ $\dfrac{42}{100} = 0.42$ $\dfrac{90}{100} = 0.9$

3. $\dfrac{4}{10}$ or $\dfrac{2}{5}$ $\dfrac{6}{10}$ or $\dfrac{3}{5}$ $\dfrac{8}{10}$ or $\dfrac{4}{5}$ $\dfrac{2}{100}$ or $\dfrac{1}{50}$ $\dfrac{5}{100}$ or $\dfrac{1}{20}$ $\dfrac{8}{100}$ or $\dfrac{2}{25}$

$\dfrac{25}{100}$ or $\dfrac{1}{4}$ $\dfrac{75}{100}$ or $\dfrac{3}{4}$ $\dfrac{22}{100}$ or $\dfrac{11}{50}$

CONVERTING TO DECIMALS WITH A CALCULATOR (PAGE 14)

1. 0.3333333   0.6666666   0.3636363   0.3846153   0.4444444   0.4285714
0.1818181   0.2307692   0.2352941   0.3333333   0.5714285   0.7777777
2. 0.27   0.11   0.17   0.83   0.64   0.85
0.57   0.56   0.52   0.93   0.88   0.41
0.41   0.35   0.82

PROPORTION (PAGE 20)

1. $\dfrac{4}{9}$ $\dfrac{1}{4}$ $\dfrac{3}{8}$ $\dfrac{3}{8}$ $\dfrac{1}{3}$

2. $\dfrac{7}{12}$ or 0.58 $\dfrac{3}{7}$ or 0.43

3. 25   12

Answers

MIXED NUMBERS AND IMPROPER FRACTIONS (PAGE 22)

1. $2\frac{2}{3}$ $\quad$ $4\frac{2}{3}$ $\quad$ $1\frac{2}{5}$ $\quad$ $2\frac{3}{8}$ $\quad$ $2\frac{3}{9}$ or $2\frac{1}{3}$ $\quad$ $1\frac{2}{7}$ $\quad$ $5\frac{3}{4}$ $\quad$ $2\frac{4}{5}$ $\quad$ $4\frac{1}{6}$ $\quad$ $4\frac{1}{2}$

$5\frac{2}{7}$ $\quad$ $6\frac{4}{5}$ $\quad$ $8\frac{2}{5}$ $\quad$ $6\frac{2}{8}$ or $6\frac{1}{4}$ $\quad$ $8\frac{7}{9}$

2. $\frac{13}{4}$ $\quad$ $\frac{23}{4}$ $\quad$ $\frac{21}{5}$ $\quad$ $\frac{14}{3}$ $\quad$ $\frac{21}{8}$ $\quad$ $\frac{19}{6}$ $\quad$ $\frac{13}{2}$ $\quad$ $\frac{25}{3}$ $\quad$ $\frac{35}{6}$ $\quad$ $\frac{31}{4}$ $\quad$ $\frac{34}{5}$ $\quad$ $\frac{19}{8}$ $\quad$ $\frac{29}{7}$ $\quad$ $\frac{32}{9}$ $\quad$ $\frac{41}{7}$

ADDING AND SUBTRACTING FRACTIONS (PAGE 24)

1. $\frac{4}{5}$ $\quad$ $\frac{6}{9}$ or $\frac{2}{3}$ $\quad$ $\frac{10}{7}$ or $1\frac{3}{7}$ $\quad$ $\frac{13}{10}$ or $1\frac{3}{10}$ $\quad$ $\frac{8}{8}$ or 1 $\quad$ $\frac{6}{4}$ or $1\frac{2}{4}$ or $1\frac{1}{2}$

$\frac{2}{11}$ $\quad$ $\frac{4}{6}$ or $\frac{2}{3}$ $\quad$ $\frac{1}{5}$ $\quad$ $\frac{8}{12}$ or $\frac{2}{3}$ $\quad$ $\frac{5}{9}$ $\quad$ $\frac{4}{13}$

2. $\frac{6}{10}$ or $\frac{3}{5}$ $\quad$ $\frac{14}{12}$ or $1\frac{2}{12}$ or $1\frac{1}{6}$ $\quad$ $\frac{11}{10}$ or $1\frac{1}{10}$ $\quad$ $\frac{27}{20}$ or $1\frac{7}{20}$ $\quad$ $\frac{1}{12}$ $\quad$ $\frac{7}{15}$ $\quad$ $\frac{9}{14}$ $\quad$ $\frac{13}{30}$

ORDERING DECIMALS (PAGE 26)

1. 0.40 $\quad$ 0.8 $\quad$ 0.82 $\quad$ 0.54 $\quad$ 0.823 $\quad$ 0.603 $\quad$ 0.9 $\quad$ 0.751 $\quad$ 0.21 $\quad$ 0.31
0.3 $\quad$ 0.863 $\quad$ 0.2741 $\quad$ 0.743

2. 0.413 $\quad$ 0.314 $\quad$ 0.3 $\quad$ 0.14 $\quad$ 0.134
0.892 $\quad$ 0.8 $\quad$ 0.29 $\quad$ 0.289 $\quad$ 0.28
0.525 $\quad$ 0.52 $\quad$ 0.5 $\quad$ 0.252 $\quad$ 0.25

ORDERING FRACTIONS (PAGE 27)

$\frac{1}{8}$ $\quad$ $\frac{1}{3}$ $\quad$ $\frac{2}{5}$ $\quad$ $\frac{3}{4}$ $\quad$ $\frac{9}{10}$

ORDERING FRACTIONS (PAGE 28)

1. $\frac{1}{8}$ $\quad$ $\frac{3}{4}$ $\quad$ $\frac{4}{5}$ $\quad$ $\frac{5}{6}$ $\quad$ $\frac{7}{8}$

$\frac{5}{10}$ $\quad$ $\frac{3}{5}$ $\quad$ $\frac{5}{8}$ $\quad$ $\frac{2}{3}$ $\quad$ $\frac{5}{6}$

$\frac{1}{8}$ $\quad$ $\frac{1}{4}$ $\quad$ $\frac{3}{10}$ $\quad$ $\frac{2}{5}$ $\quad$ $\frac{2}{3}$

$\frac{1}{2}$ $\quad$ $\frac{5}{8}$ $\quad$ $\frac{4}{6}$ $\quad$ $\frac{7}{10}$ $\quad$ $\frac{3}{4}$

2. 0.8 $\quad$ 0.786 $\quad$ 0.9 $\quad$ 0.846 $\quad$ 0.833 $\quad$ 0.714
$\frac{5}{7}$ $\quad$ $\frac{11}{14}$ $\quad$ $\frac{4}{5}$ $\quad$ $\frac{10}{12}$ $\quad$ $\frac{11}{13}$ $\quad$ $\frac{9}{10}$

0.222 $\quad$ 0.429 $\quad$ 0.364 $\quad$ 0.083 $\quad$ 0.353 $\quad$ 0.333
$\frac{1}{12}$ $\quad$ $\frac{2}{9}$ $\quad$ $\frac{2}{6}$ $\quad$ $\frac{6}{17}$ $\quad$ $\frac{4}{11}$ $\quad$ $\frac{3}{7}$

COMMON DENOMINATORS (PAGE 30)

1. $\frac{28}{36}$ $\quad$ $\frac{27}{36}$ $\quad$ $\frac{30}{36}$ $\quad$ $\frac{33}{36}$ $\quad$ $\frac{24}{36}$

2. $\frac{3}{5} = \frac{24}{40}$ $\quad$ $\frac{5}{8} = \frac{25}{40}$ $\quad$ $\frac{13}{20} = \frac{26}{40}$

$\frac{1}{12} = \frac{2}{24}$ $\quad$ $\frac{2}{6} = \frac{8}{24}$ $\quad$ $\frac{3}{8} = \frac{9}{24}$ $\quad$ $\frac{2}{3} = \frac{16}{24}$

$\frac{2}{3} = \frac{30}{45}$ $\quad$ $\frac{7}{9} = \frac{35}{45}$ $\quad$ $\frac{4}{5} = \frac{36}{45}$ $\quad$ $\frac{13}{15} = \frac{39}{45}$